I

COLOURING
PATTERNS

Buster Books

Illustrated by
Beth Gunnell, Jessie Eckel
and Cindy Wilde

Designed by
Zoe Bradley
and
Angie Allison

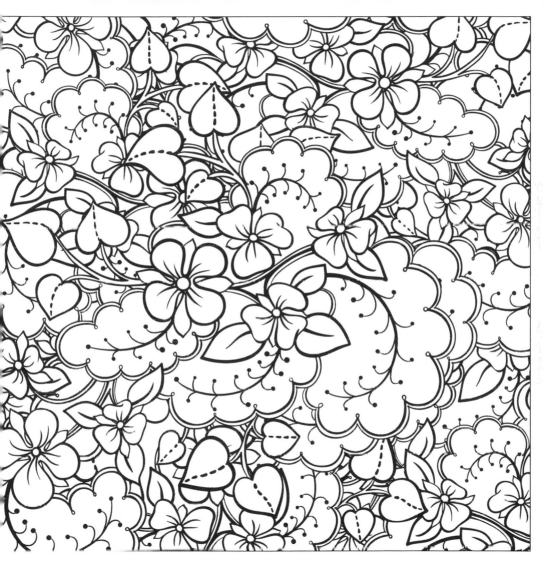

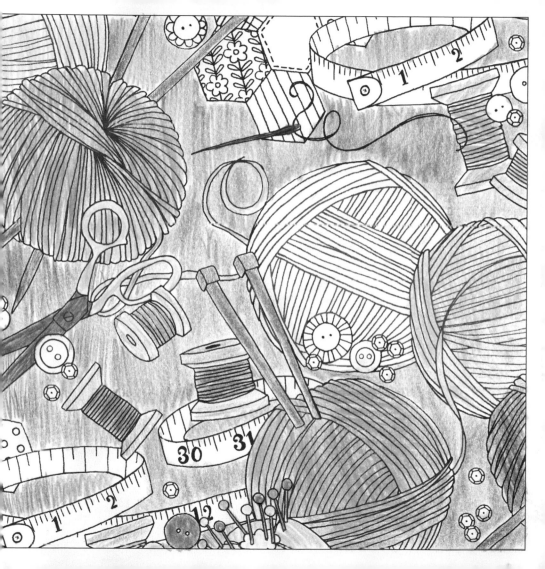

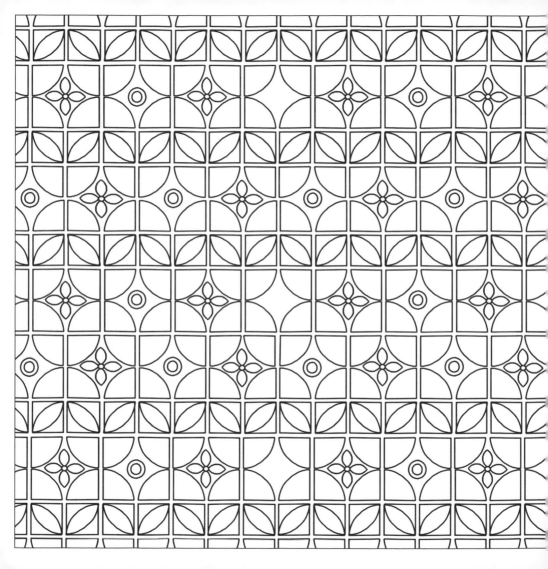

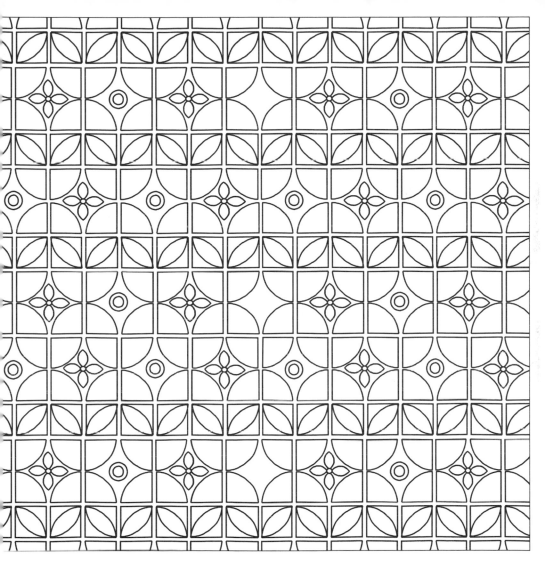

First published in Great Britain in 2015 by Buster Books, an imprint of
Michael O'Mara Books Limited, 9 Lion Yard, Tremadoc Road, London SW4 7NQ

The pictures in this book previously appeared in the following: *Pretty Patterns Colouring Book*,
Perfect Patterns Colouring Book, *The Pattern Colouring Book*, *Beautiful Copycat Colouring*

With additional material adapted from www.shutterstock.com

W www.busterbooks.co.uk   Buster Children's Books   @BusterBooks

ISBN: 978-1-78055-406-8

4 6 8 10 9 7 5

This book was printed in September 2015 by L.E.G.O., Viale dell'Industria 2, 36100, Vicenza, Italy.